It's never too late to sing

CHRISTMAS

HEIDI PEGLER AND PAM WEDGWOOD

FABER ff MUSIC

This edition first published in 2012 by Faber Music Ltd
Bloomsbury House
74–77 Great Russell Street
London WC1B 3DA
Music processed by Jackie Leigh
Cover design by Lydia Merrills-Ashcroft
CD produced by Oliver Wedgwood
Cover photograph © Hemera/thinkstock
Printed in England by Caligraving Ltd

ISBN10: 0-571-53719-7
EAN13: 978-0-571-53719-8

Contents

The CD

The CD contains piano accompaniments for all the songs. Where necessary, the vocal line is played by an instrumental sound to help you follow your part and sing along.

Practice tips

1 Quem pastores laudavere

- This song is in four-bar phrases so you need to take quick, short breaths after 'other', 'mother', 'brother', etc. Make sure the breaths are not audible otherwise the feeling of the song will become quite frantic and that is not the mood you want to convey.
- There is a key change into the last verse (bars 42–43) so listen to the CD carefully. You will need more energy to keep the sound strong here, although the end of the song reverts to a gentle feel.
- Watch out for the rhythm in bars 62–63 – there are two beats on each note.
- You have a choice of note at the end – a G or a B – it's up to you!

2 Have yourself a merry little Christmas

- There are several changes of time in this song. The opening section (bars 5–12) is quite conversational and perhaps not as well known, so listen to the CD carefully.
- The main melody starting at bar 13 should be sung in a relaxed way. Don't put too much weight on the lower notes as this will make the transition in the rising melody trickier to negotiate.
- Aim for a supported and sustained note in bars 43–44 on the word 'how' and also on 'now' (bars 47–48). Tuck in the diphthong at the last minute (if you are not sure what this is, see page 19 in *It's never too late to sing).*

3 Last Christmas

- This song needs to be sung with energy and bounce. The rhythms are quite syncopated but the CD will help you.
- There is an optional vocalise in the middle of the song. Try imitating the sound of an instrument as you vocalise this section.
- The last verse (bar 33) does not start on the first beat of the bar so take care that you don't jump in too early.
- The final line builds up for a big finish and again you have a choice of note at the end.

4 The little drummer boy

- This song starts softly then builds and builds, until the climax at the key change in bar 31. There can be a tendency to swoop onto the first note of each phrase so make sure you start exactly on the pitch.
- The 'pa-rum pum pum pum' phrases can be a little detached to contrast with the smooth, narrative melody sections.
- There is scope for the melody to have a feeling of rise and fall in dynamic so aim for these expressive qualities as you sing.
- The melody is played an octave higher in the piano part but the CD has a guide line that will help you.

5 Mistletoe and wine

- This song dances along at a lovely pace and is hard to sing without a smile on your face, so enjoy!
- The words are very important as they are so descriptive: do take time to emphasise special and expressive moments in the text.
- Watch out for the word underlay in verses 2 and 3 – the CD will help you here. The tiny notes refer to the melody for verse 3.
- Don't forget that the last chorus is repeated – aim for a big finish!

[6] Sussex carol (On Christmas night)

- The words need to be crisp, clear and light throughout this sparkly song.
- Aim for a long note at bars 24–25 – try not to cut it short.
- In the final verse the piano has a descant melody over the tune – don't be put off if you hear something other than your melody line.
- It might be worth snatching a breath before the final 'Amen' so this last note sounds strong and clear right to the very end.

[7] The holly and the ivy

- This famous carol travels along at a lively speed so watch out!
- Try and make a difference between the verses – they should all take on different moods and characteristics. Dynamic changes will help, but you could also vary the articulation for example, by making verse 3 smooth and verse 4 detached and bouncy.
- There is an extra tag at the end of the song. If you are not sure how it goes, listen to the CD carefully – it will help you and you can decide whether you want to sing high or low at the end.

[8] Silent night

- Aim for lovely long vowel sounds in this piece so the performance is smooth and sustained throughout.
- The music is sometimes phrased in two bars and sometimes in four depending on the sense of the words. For example, try to sing bars 13–16 in one breath and also bars 17-20.
- Don't forget to use your abdominal support as you sing up to the note in bar 24 – draw your abdominal muscles towards your backbone but then release them again as you breathe for the next phrase.

[9] Christmas song (Merry Christmas to you)

- This song has an octave leap right at the start so anticipate this jump by finding lots of space at the back of the throat - a feeling of surprise!
- There are quite a few chromatic phrases where the melody is moving by small semitone steps. Be very careful that you get the pitch exactly right and if you are not sure, listen to the CD.
- Make sure you hold the first note in bar 21 ('Santa') for two-and-a-half beats: count to beat three before you move down the scale.
- Once you have the melody secure, sing it in a relaxed style and take your time at the end.

[10] The Angel Gabriel

- This song is in compound time, so there are either three beats in a bar or four beats where the time signature changes.
- The song tells a story so try to bring out the characters by giving them each a different vocal colour – the Narrator, the Angel Gabriel and Mary.
- The vocal line becomes independent of the piano part in the third and fourth verses – watch out!
- The song has a strong finish and there is a change from the minor to a major key chord at the very end to leave us feeling optimistic for the future.

11 Santa Claus is comin' to town

- The chorus of this song is very familiar but the opening verse might be less so. It is conversational in style so watch out for the changes of time. The melody jumps about but the CD can help you here.
- The main chorus is in a boogie-woogie style: have fun!
- The middle eight lies slightly high so you will need to be mentally prepared for this section and allow for lots of space at the back of the throat (bars 34–42).
  The very last section (bars 43–46) is sung really quietly to contrast with the last line where the melody explodes out again.

12 A medley of Christmas cheer

- This final arrangement incorporates three famous Christmas songs – *Deck the halls*, *Good King Wenceslas* and *We wish you a merry Christmas*.
- The opening song bounces along at a good pace. The 'fa la la' sections are a good warm-up for the tongue, and the breaths need to be quick and energetic to keep this moving in time.
- *Good King Wenceslas* is in a boogie style and again the music is quick and lively. Have fun with the voice of the King in verse 2 in contrast to that of the Page.
- The final song needs no introduction and again you have a choice of note at the end. It is worth snatching a quick breath after 'Christmas' so the end is strong and exciting. Have fun!

Quemn pastores laudavere

piano accompaniment

Traditional

24
f
3. Wise men came from far and saw Him, Knelt in
f
29
ho - mage to a - dore Him. Pre - cious gifts they lay be -
35
- fore Him: Gold and fran - kin - cense and myrrh.
mp
41
poco rit.
a tempo
f
4. Let us now in ev - 'ry na - tion
f

47
Sing His praise with ex - ul - ta - tion. All the
52
world shall find sal - va - tion In the birth of Ma - ry's
58
son. In the birth of Ma - - ry's
mp
mp
64
son. Hmm.

Have yourself a merry little Christmas

2 piano accompaniment

Words and Music by Hugh Martin and Ralph Blane

13
slowly (in strict time)
Have your-self a mer-ry lit-tle Christ-mas, let your heart be light,
Next year all our
18
trou-bles will be out of sight.
Have your-self a mer-ry lit-tle Christ-mas,
23
make the Yule-tide gay,
Next year all our trou-bles will be miles a - way.
28
Once a-gain as in old-en days, hap-py gold-en days of yore.
mf
mp

33
Faith - ful friends who were dear to us will be near to us once more.
37
Some day soon we all will be to - ge - ther, if the Fates al - low,
41
Un - til then we'll have to mud - dle through some - how.
So
45
rall.
have your - self a mer - ry lit - tle Christ - mas now.

Last Christmas

piano accompaniment

Words and Music by George Michael

15
give it to some - one spe - cial.
Last Christ - mas I
18
gave you my heart, but the ve - ry next day you gave it a - way.
21
This year to save me from tears I'll give it to some - one spe -
24
Opt.
- cial.
Wah wah...
mp

28
mf
31
mf
Once bit - ten and
mf
34
twice shy,
I keep my dis - tance but you still catch my eye,
37
Tell me ba - by, do you re - cog - nise me?
Well, it's been a year, it

40
does - n't sur - prise me.
I wrapped it up and sent it
43
with a note say - ing 'I love you', I meant it.
Now I know what a fool
46
I've been but if you kissed me now I know you'd fool me a - gain.
poco rit.
49
p
f
Last Christ - mas, last Christ - mas, last Christ - mas.
f

The little drummer boy

piano accompaniment

Words and Music by Katherine Davis, Henry Onorati and Harry Simeone

13
-rum pum pum pum, To lay be - fore the King, pa -
-rum pum pum pum, That's fit to give a King, pa -
17
-rum pum pum pum, rum pum pum pum, rum pum pum pum.
-rum pum pum pum, rum pum pum pum, rum pum pum pum.
21
So to ho - nour Him, pa - rum pum pum pum,
Shall I play for you, pa - rum pum pum pum,
25
1.
when we come.

29
2.
on my drum?
Ma - - ry nod - ded, pa -
33
-rum pum pum pum,
The ox and
36
lamb kept time, pa - rum pum pum pum,
I played my
40
drum for Him, pa - rum pum pum pum,

43
I played my best for Him, pa - rum pum pum pum,
46
rum pum pum pum, rum pum pum pum.
Then He
50
smiled at me, pa - rum pum pum pum,
53
Me and my drum.
Me and my drum.

Mistletoe and wine

(5) piano accompaniment

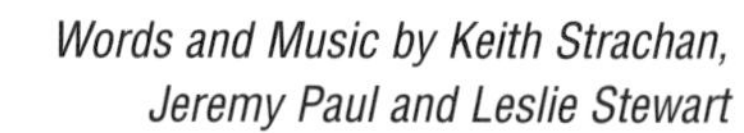

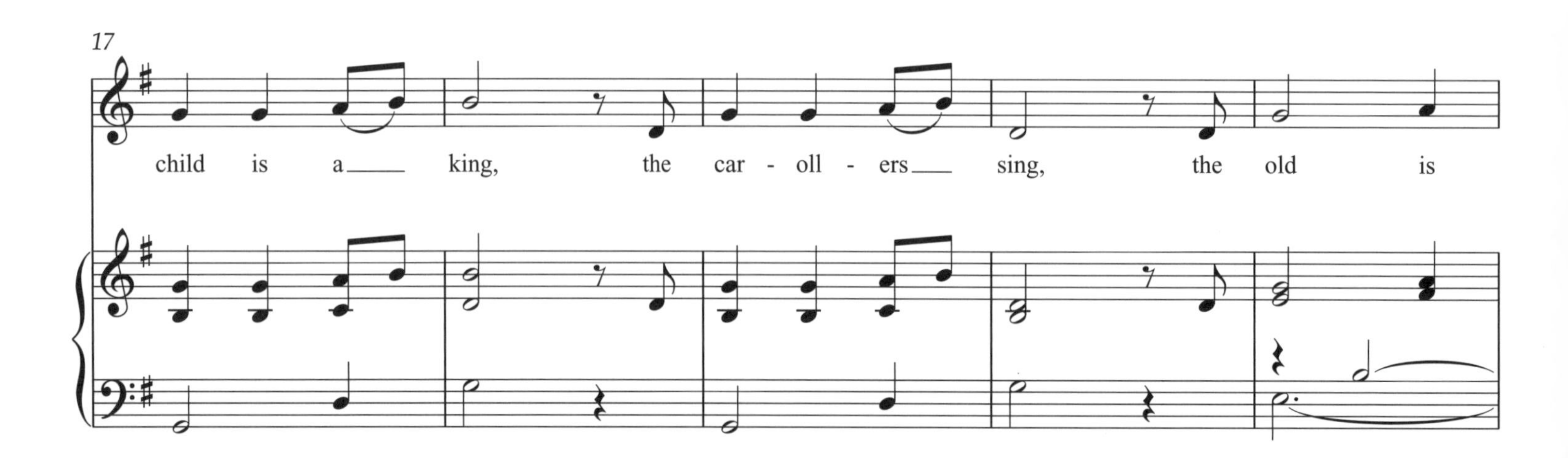

22
passed, there's a new be - gin - ning. Dreams of San - ta,
27
dreams of snow, fin - gers numb, fac - es a - glow. It's
33
mf
Christ - mas time, mis - tle - toe and wine, child - ren
mf
38
sing - ing Chris - ti - an rhyme with logs on the fire and

43
gifts on the tree; A time to re - joice in the good that we
48
see. 2. A time for liv - ing, a time for be - liev - ing, a
see. 3. It's a time for giv - ing, a time for get - ting, a
53
time for trust - ing, not de - ceiv - ing.
time for for - giv - ing, and for for - get - ting.
57
Love and laugh - ter and joy ev - er af - ter Ours for the
Christ - mas is love, Christ - mas is peace; A time for

62
1.
2.
tak - ing just fol - low the mas - ter. cease. Christ - mas
hat - ing and fight - ing to
67
time, mis - tle - toe and wine, child - ren sing - ing
72
Chris - ti - an rhyme with logs on the fire and gifts on the
77
1.
2.
tree; A time to re - joice in the good that we see. see.

Sussex carol (On Christmas night)

6 piano accompaniment

15
Christ - mas night all Christ - ians sing To hear the news the an - gels bring.
sin de - parts be - fore thy grace Then life and health come in its place.
19
mp
News of great joy, news of great mirth,
An - gels and men with joy may sing,
mf
News of our
All for to
mp
mf
23
mer - ci - ful King's birth.
see our new - born King!
mp
27
mf 2. When
f 3. From

32
out of dark - ness we have light Which made the an - gels sing that night, From
f
36
out of dark - ness we have light Which made the an - gels sing that night,
40
mp
'Glo - ry to God and peace to men
f
Now and for -
mp
f
44
-ev - er - more, A - men!'

The holly and the ivy

piano accompaniment

13
mp
ris - ing of the sun and the run - ning of the deer, The play - ing of the
mp
18
f
mer - ry or - gan, sweet sing - ing in the choir.
f
p
cresc.
23
mp
2. 3. 4. 5. The
mp
29
mf
hol - ly bears a bark as bit - ter as a - ny gall, And Ma - ry bore sweet
mf

34
Je - sus Christ for to re - deem us all. Oh the ris - ing of the
38
sun and the run - ning of the deer, The play - ing of the
42
mer - ry or - gan, sweet sing - ing in the choir. The hol - ly and the
46
cresc.
poco rit.
i - vy when they are full grown, The hol - ly bears the crown.

Silent night

piano accompaniment

Words by Joseph Mohr
Music by Franz Xavier Gruber

17
p
Ho - ly in - fant so Ten - der and mild, Sleep in
Heav - 'nly hosts sing 'Al - le - lu - ia', Christ the
p
22
hea - ven - ly peace,
Sa - viour is born,
Sleep in hea - ven - ly
Christ the Sa - viour is
27
peace.
born.
p
32
mp
3. Si - lent night, Ho - ly night,
mp

37
p
Son of God, Love's pure light, Ra - dient
p
42
beams from thy Ho - ly face, With the dawn of Re -
47
cresc.
- deem - ing grace, Je - sus, Lord at thy birth,
cresc.
52
poco rit.
p
Je - sus, Lord at thy birth.
p

Christmas song (Merry Christmas to you)

(9) piano accompaniment

Words and Music by Mel Tormé and Robert Wells

12
mp
-mos. Ev-'ry-bo-dy knows a tur-key and some mis-tle-toe, Help to make the sea-son
mp
16
3
bright. Ti-ny tots with their eyes all a-glow Will find it hard to sleep to-
3
20
mf
-night. They know that San - ta's on his way, He's load-ed
mf
23
p
lots of toys and good-ies on his sleigh, And ev-'ry mo-ther's child is gon-na
p

26
spy To see if rein - deers real - ly know how to fly. And
29
mp
so I'm of - fer - ing this sim - ple phrase, To kids from one to nine - ty -
mp
32
- two. Al - though it's been said ma - ny times, ma - ny ways, 'Mer - ry
cresc.
35
mf
Christ - mas to you. Mer - ry Christ - mas to you.'
p
rit.
mf
p

The Angel Gabriel

piano accompaniment

Traditional

hail,' said he 'thou low - ly mai - den Ma - ry, Most high - ly fa - voured la - dy.'
Glo - ri - a!
2. 'For know a bles - sed Mo - ther thou shalt be, All
ge - ne-ra - tions laud and ho - nour thee, Thy Son shall be Em ma - nu - el by

20
mf
p
seers fore - told, Most high - ly fa - voured la - dy.' Glo - - - ri -
mf
p
23
p
- a! 3. Then
mp
p
26
gen - tle Ma - ry meek - ly bowed her head, 'To me be as it pleas - eth
29
mp
God,' she said, 'My soul shall laud and mag - ni - fy His ho - ly name,' Most
mp

32
p
mf
high - ly fa - voured la - dy. Glo - - - ri - a! 4. Of
p
mf
35
her, Em - ma - nu - el, the Christ, was born, In Beth - le - hem, all on a
38
f
Christ - mas morn, And Christ - ian folks through - out the world will ev - er say, 'Most
f
41
high - ly fa - voured la - dy.' Glo - - - ri - a!
Ped.

Santa Claus is comin' to town

piano accompaniment

Words by Haven Gillespie
Music by J. Fred Coots

poco rit.
a tempo
16
mp
- day. I called on dear old San - ta Claus to see what I could see, He
mf
21
poco rit.
With a really good swing
took me to his work-shop And told his plans to me. 1. So you bet - ter watch out, you
(2.) ma - king a list, he's
f
26
bet - ter not cry, you bet - ter not pout I'm tell - ing you why:
check-ing it twice, he's gon - na find out who's naugh - ty or nice.
San - ta Claus is
30
1.
2.
com - in' to town. 2. He's town.

34
mf
He sees you when you're sleep - ing, he knows when you're a -
mf
38
- wake, he knows if you've been bad or good, so be good for good - ness
42
whisper
p
sake! So, you'd bet - ter watch out, you bet - ter not cry, you bet - ter not pout, I'm
p
46
tell ing you why: San - ta Claus is com - in' to town!
ff
Yeah!
ff

A medley of Christmas cheer

12 piano accompaniment

Traditional

14
poco rit.
D.S. 𝄋
Christ-mas ca - rol,
Christ-mas trea - sure
Fa la la la la, la la la la.
19
𝄋𝄋 Boogie-style
f
1. Good King Wen - ces - las looked out
When the snow lay round a - bout,
2. 'Hi - ther, page, and stand by me,
Yon - der pea - sant, who is he?
On the feast of Ste - phen,
Deep and crisp and e - ven.
If thou know'st it tell - ing,
Where and what his dwell - ing?'
23
mp
(1.) Bright - ly shone the moon that night,
(2.) 'Sire he lives a good league hence,
Though the frost was cru - el,
Un - der - neath the moun - tain,
When a poor man
Right a - gainst the
28
f
1.
D.S. 𝄋𝄋
came in sight,
fo - rest fence,
Ga - th'ring win - ter fu - el.
By Saint Agn - es' foun -

33
2.
mf
-tain.' 1. We wish you a mer-ry Christ-mas, We wish you a mer-ry
38
mp
Christ - mas, We wish you a mer - ry Christ - mas, And a Hap - py New Year! Good
43
ti - dings we bring To you and your kin, We wish you a mer - ry
48
f
Christ - mas And a Hap - py New Year!
mf

53
mf
2. So bring us some fig - gy pud - ding, So bring us some fig - gy pud - ding, So
58
mp
bring us some fig - gy pud - ding, And bring some out here! Good ti - dings we
mp
63
bring To you and your kin, We wish you a mer - ry Christ - mas And a
68
f
Hap - py New Year!
f
ff